TIGER MOTH
KUNG POW
CHICKEN

by Aaron Reynolds
illustrated by
Erik Lervold

CAST OF CHARACTERS

Tiger Moth

Kung Pow

Hey, what's that?

I bet my left wing it's Weevil, the baddest of all bugs.

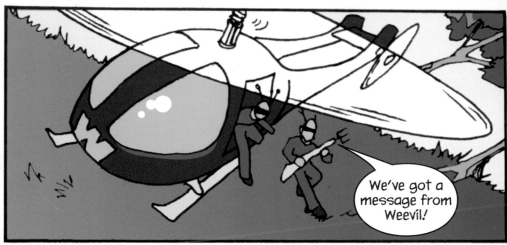

We've got a message from Weevil!

How did you know?

It's a gift. That and the big "W" on the helicopter.

Right.

So, what's the message?

Weevil would like to give it to you . . . in person!

Run!

What about the other one?

Weevil's not interested in that little chicken.

Of course, that wasn't the time to point out that I'm a woodlouse, not a chicken.

TIGER!!!

Tiger's at the mercy of that psycho, Weevil.

I'm standing here in class doing nothing about it.

But what can I do? I'm just an apprentice.

And a little scared . . .

Maybe those two baddies were right. Am I just chicken?

14

When two birds fly, only one stone can be thrown.

What?

Two are better than one! That's what I'm trying to say here!

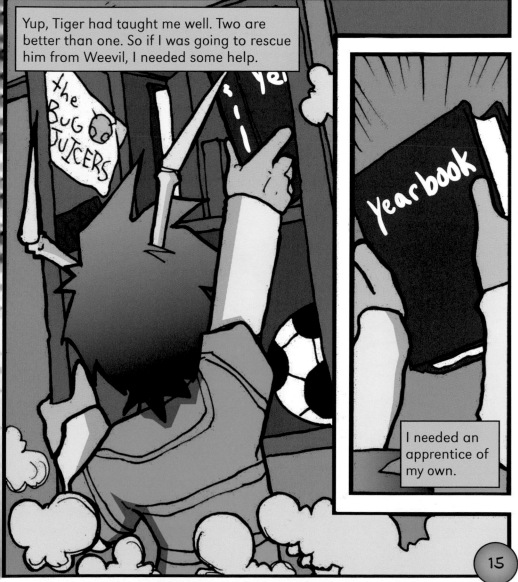

Yup, Tiger had taught me well. Two are better than one. So if I was going to rescue him from Weevil, I needed some help.

the BUG JUICERS

Yearbook

I needed an apprentice of my own.

And the choices are . . .

Mrs Mandible? No good. Grown-ups have this weird thing about not letting kids get into danger.

The Fruit Fly Boys? I might as well fly straight into a bug zapper.

Dragon? The right amount of muscle, but I doubt he can play nicely with others.

18

I had asked Tiger the same question not long ago . . .

A smart ninja blends technology with skill.

What do you mean?

From now on, we'll keep these on us at all times.

What are they?

Homing devices. They'll pinpoint our exact location to each other.

Because of that whole "two bamboos when the wind blows" thing, right?

Any more questions, little sister?

Yeah, is there anything Tiger didn't teach you?

We're about to find out.

19

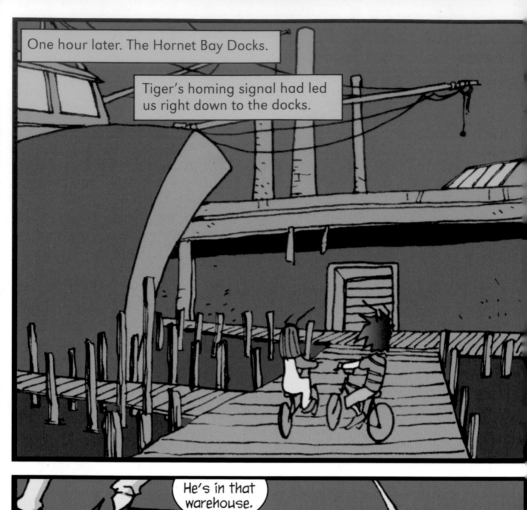

One hour later. The Hornet Bay Docks.

Tiger's homing signal had led us right down to the docks.

He's in that warehouse.

Well, let's get him!

Slow down, grasshopper.

I'm a woodlouse.

Whatever.

Listen closely, apprentice.

A ninja is silent and invisible. We must see without being seen.

Now follow me and keep quiet.

BLING!

Yes, master.

I had to admit, I liked the sound of that.

22

Your tiger stripes will not shine quite so brightly!

And you will foil my plans no longer!

MWAH HA HA!

Boss, wouldn't it be easier to just cut the rope and let the spiders eat him now?

Yeah. How come we have to lower him slowly while you stand here and talk about his certain doom?

Because, you fools!

This way is much more evil!

Oh yeah. I keep forgetting that.

23

Outside . . .

It's a harmless little girl.

What's wrong, honey?

SNIFF SNIFF

I'm I-I-I-lost!

Awwww! We'll help you!

I have a better idea.

Hi-yah!

Harmless little girl? Think again, boys.

SPLASH!

SPLOOSH!

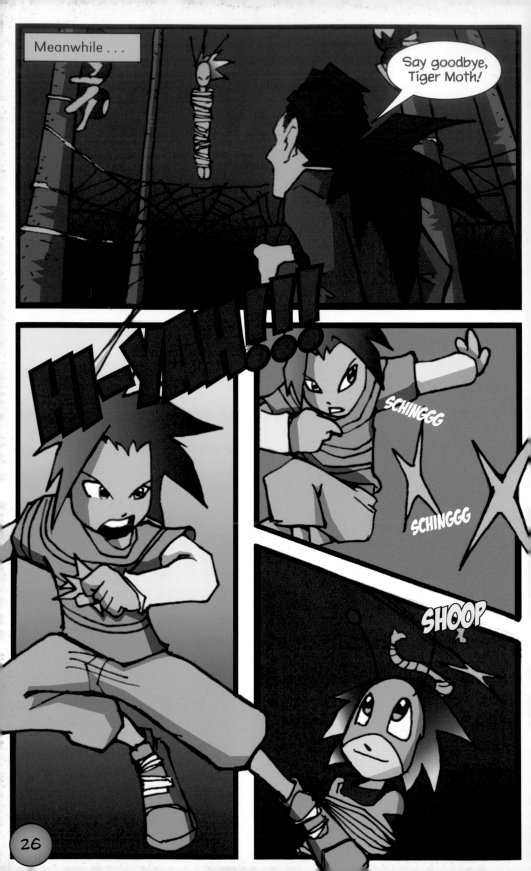

31

And so, I rescued Tiger, all by myself.

Hello? Don't forget me!

Okay, fine! I had a little help from my new apprentice.

Not bad, Kung. Not bad at all.

What do you mean "not bad"?

I saved your exoskeleton.

You certainly did.

And do you know my favourite part of your plan?

Having Amber create a distraction?

No. It's how you ran away when they got me in the helicopter.

What?!

32

33

ABOUT THE AUTHOR

Aaron Reynolds loves insects and loves books, so Tiger Moth was a perfect blend of both. Reynolds is the author of several great books for children, including *Chicks and Salsa,* which *Publishers Weekly* called "a literary fandango." Reynolds had no idea what a "fandango" was, but after looking it up in the dictionary (it means "playful and silly behaviour"), he hopes to write several more fandangos in the future. He lives with his wife, two children, and four insect-obsessed cats.

ABOUT THE ILLUSTRATOR

Erik Lervold was born in Puerto Rico, a small island in the Caribbean, and has been a professional painter. Deciding that he wanted to be a full-time artist, he attended the Minneapolis College of Art and Design, studied Comic Art, and graduated in 2004. Lervold teaches classes in libraries and has taught art in the Minnesota Children's Museum. He loves the colour green and has a collection of really big goggles. He also loves sandwiches. If you want him to be your friend, bring him a roast beef sandwich and he will love you forever.

GLOSSARY

apprentice young person (or insect) that learns a skill from a more experienced person (or insect)

bamboo tropical plant with a woody stem

beeline straightest, fastest way from one place to another

distraction something that keeps a person from thinking about what they're doing

exoskeleton bony shell covering the outside of some insects

gizzard inside part of a chicken or an insect. When someone says, "That sticks in my gizzard", they really mean that something bothers them.

henchman person (or insect) who helps his or her evil master

homing device gadget used for locating a person or place

professional someone good enough at an activity to make it a career

villain evil person or insect

MORE ABOUT SPIDERS

Did you know that spiders aren't actually insects?
That's right. They belong to a different group
called Arachnida. Most insects have three main
body parts and six legs. Most spiders, on the other hand,
have only two main parts to their body and eight legs.

Scientists have discovered more than 37,000 species,
or different types of spiders . . . so far. They believe that
possibly only a quarter of the total number of species
have been found.

The Goliath bird-eating spider is the largest spider in the
world. Measuring over 30 centimetres (12 inches) across, this
giant monster feeds on frogs, snakes, insects, lizards, and
some small birds. But don't worry. Goliath bird-eating spiders
are found deep within the South American rainforest and
aren't very harmful to humans.

Golden orb web spiders aren't the largest spiders, but they
can spin the largest webs. Often lasting for several years,
their webs can stretch almost 2 metres (6 feet) wide and over
6 metres (20 feet) high!

Thousands of spiders working together created the largest web ever found. According to the *Guinness Book of World Records,* money spiders built a 4.5 hectare web that covered an entire school playing field in Warwick.

Spiders aren't poisonous, but they are venomous. So what's the difference? Poisonous animals can be harmful if they are eaten or even touched. Venomous animals must bite or inject harmful substances into their victims.

One of the deadliest spiders in the world is the Brazilian wandering spider. This spider is also known as the banana spider because it's been found in bunches of bananas.

Spiders aren't all that bad, though. In fact, each spider eats about 2,000 insects every year. So they actually help keep your home pest-free!

Spiders can also be a tasty treat. In some Asian countries, they are seasoned and deep-fried for a roadside snack.

DISCUSSION QUESTIONS

1. Describe some of the ways Kung Pow's little sister, Amber, helped him. Do you think he could have saved Tiger Moth without her? Why or why not?

2. At the beginning of the story, Kung Pow was afraid to rescue Tiger Moth because he didn't think he was ready. Have you ever been afraid to take a test or complete a challenge? Describe the experience and how you fought through your fear.

3. Now that Kung Pow has saved Tiger Moth, do you think he's ready to battle evil insects by himself?

WRITING PROMPTS

1. Kung Pow has learned a lot from Tiger Moth. Choose one person that you've learned a lot from, and then write a story about him or her.

2. In the end, Weevil escapes to his headquarters. Pretend you're the author, and write a story where Tiger Moth and Kung Pow find his hide-away. Imagine what happens next.

3. This Tiger Moth book was based around the character of Kung Pow. Choose your own favourite Tiger Moth character, such as the Fly Boys, Amber, Mrs Mandible, or even Weevil, and write a story about them.

More amazing adventures!

When Zack Allen is bullied at school, he invents a robot super suit to help him fight evil in the playground and beyond. He becomes Zinc Alloy, the world's newest superhero!